Read, Search & Find®

Kidsbooks®

2 Church Green, Witney, Oxon OX28 4AW

Illustrated by Peter Dennis (Linda Rogers Associates)

3535 West Peterson Avenue
Chicago, IL 60659

Printed in China
121203001SZ

Contents

Introduction 5
Dinosaurs 6–7
Seasons 8–9
Polar Regions 10–11
Forest 12–13
Rain Forest 14–15
Desert 16–17
Ocean Life 18–19
African Grassland 20–21
Mountains 22–23
Under the Ground 24–25
Find Out More 26–31

Introduction

Many fascinating animals and interesting plants can be found in rain forests, deserts, and rugged mountains.

WILD WONDERS takes you to faraway destinations and shows how nature lives in harmony. You'll discover through colorful illustrations and fun search & find® activities how plants and animals survive in extreme climates. You will see beautiful and detailed images of animals in their natural habitats—digging, diving, running, and hunting.

In the back of this book, you can explore the **Find Out More** section. Here, you will discover even more fun facts about animals and their habitats.

So, get your camera and get ready to **Read, Search & Find®** as you discover

WILD WONDERS!

Dinosaurs

Dinosaurs roamed Earth millions of years ago. There were many different kinds of dinosaurs. Some were huge. Others were very small. Some dinosaurs ate meat. Other dinosaurs ate plants. Flying reptiles and sea creatures lived during this time, too.

Search & Find®

- ☐ *Apatosauruses* (6)
- ☐ Dinosaur footprints
- ☐ Flying reptiles (4)
- ☐ *Liopleurodon*
- ☐ *Stegosauruses* (4)
- ☐ Volcanoes (2)

Liopleurodon
(LIE-oh-PLOO-roh-don)
This huge sea reptile had a large head and long flippers.

Diplodocus
(dih-PLUH-doh-kus)
This was one of the longest dinosaurs. Its neck was 26 feet long. It could eat leaves from the tops of trees.

Compsognathus
(COMP-sug-NAY-thus)
This swift hunter was about the size of a house cat.

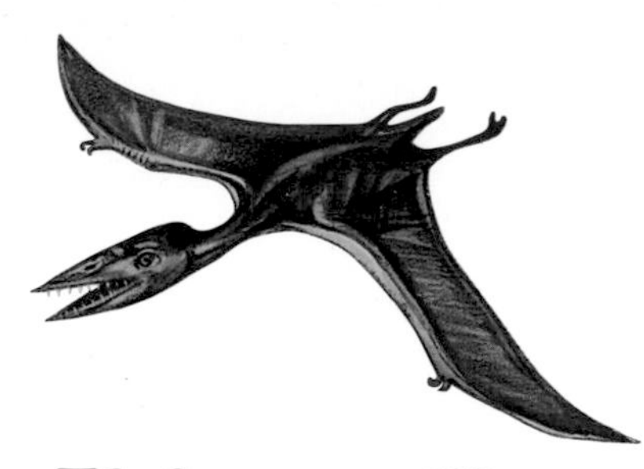

Flying reptile
Reptiles with wings flew throughout the time of the dinosaurs.

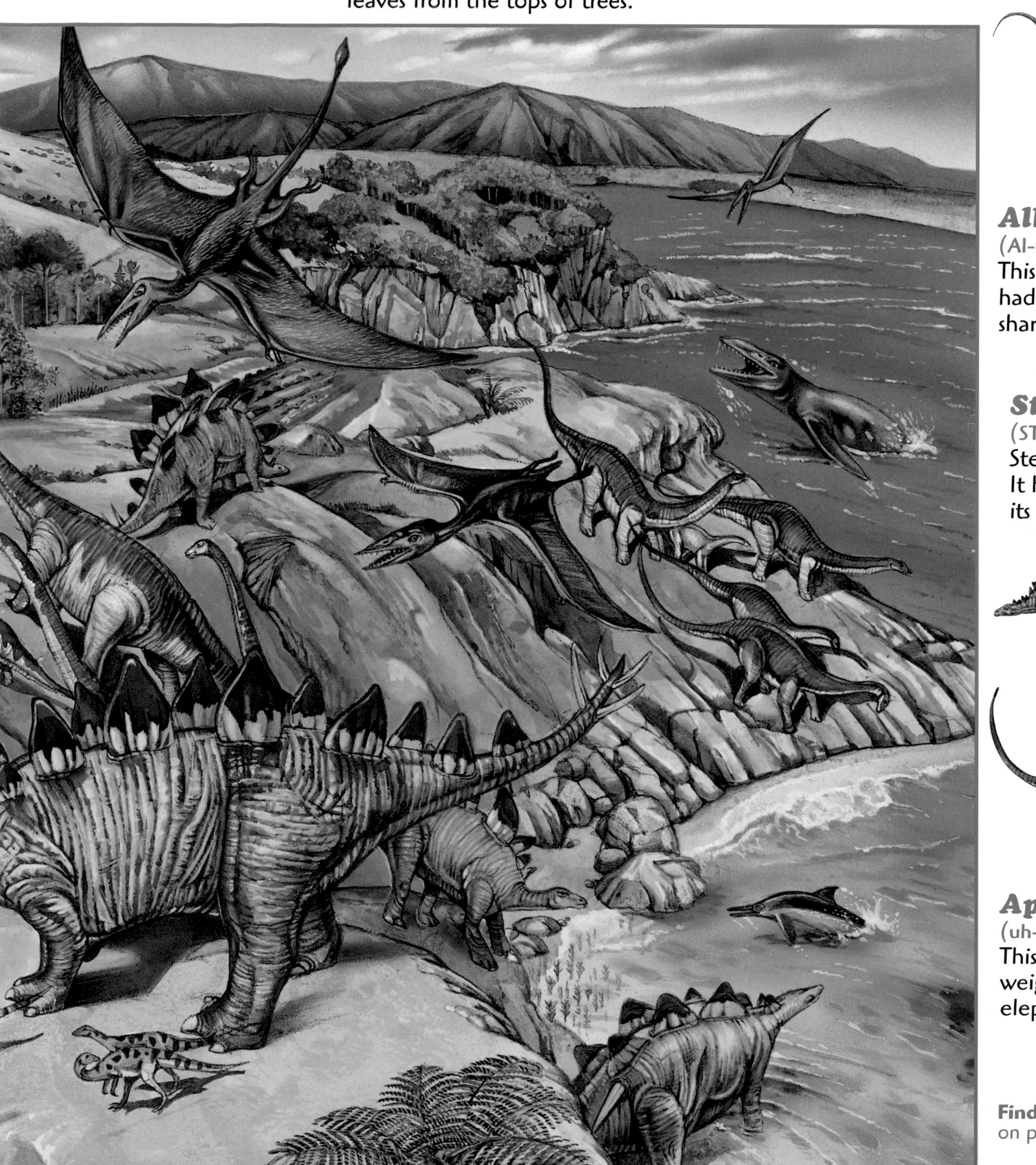

Allosaurus
(Al-uh-SORE-us)
This fierce meat eater had more than 70 sharp teeth.

Stegosaurus
(STEG-uh-SORE-us)
Stegosaurus ate plants. It had bony plates on its back.

Apatosaurus
(uh-PAT-uh-SORE-us)
This giant plant eater weighed as much as six elephants!

Find Out More
on page 26

Seasons

There are four seasons: spring, summer, autumn, and winter. In spring, flowers and plants bloom. In summer, crops grow in the fields. In autumn, leaves on some trees change color and crops are harvested. In winter, animals such as squirrels find safe places to keep warm. In some places it snows.

Search & Find®

- ☐ Baby birds (2)
- ☐ Bales of hay (3)
- ☐ Ducklings (3)
- ☐ Empty bird nest
- ☐ Foxes (4)
- ☐ Mushrooms (7)

Lambs

Lambs are usually born in the spring.

Food stored for winter

Some animals collect nuts and seeds in the fall. They save them for winter, when food is hard to find.

Flowers blooming

Many flowers bloom in spring and summer.

Rabbits
Rabbits have thick, soft fur and large ears. They eat leaves, twigs, grass, and bark.

Bird nest
Baby birds are born in the spring. They stay in the nest until they can fly.

Leaves changing color
Colder weather and less sunlight make some leaves change color. Evergreen trees stay green all year.

Sleeping squirrels
In winter, a group of squirrels may share a nest to keep warm.

Holly branch
Holly branches are often used as holiday decorations.

Snowman
The world's tallest snowman was built in Maine and stood over 113 feet tall!

Find Out More
on page 27

Polar Regions

It is very cold at the North and South Poles. The region at the North Pole is called the Arctic. The region at the South Pole is called Antarctica. Polar animals need ways to keep warm. Some have a thick layer of fat, called blubber. Others have thick fur to keep out the cold.

Search & Find®

- ☐ Arctic hares (3)
- ☐ Bird with a fish
- ☐ Hare tracks
- ☐ Killer whales (orcas) (5)
- ☐ Penguin nest
- ☐ Polar bears (4)
- ☐ Swimming seals (3)

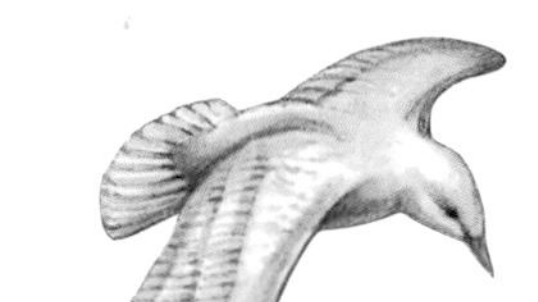

Arctic gull
Arctic gulls feed on fish. There are lots of fish in Arctic waters.

Penguin
A penguin is a bird that can't fly, but it's a great swimmer because it has wings shaped like flippers.

Elephant seal
This huge seal has a large nose that is almost like an elephant's trunk.

Walrus
Walruses have long tusks. The tusks can grow as long as three feet!

Arctic fox
The fur of an arctic fox changes color. The fur is white in the winter and grayish brown in the summer.

Emperor penguins
The emperor penguin is the largest penguin. It can be three to four feet tall and weigh about 90 pounds.

Polar bear cubs
A female polar bear will usually give birth to twin cubs.

Find Out More
on page 27

Forest

Lots of creatures live in the forest. Owls live in trees and come out only at night. Rabbits and squirrels live on the forest floor. They are active during the day. Most birds build their nests on branches. Others nest in patches of leaves on the ground. Many animals have fur or feathers that blend in with the colors of the forest.

Search & Find®

- ☐ Birds in flight (5)
- ☐ Chipmunk
- ☐ Fawns (2)
- ☐ Mouse
- ☐ Mushrooms (5)
- ☐ Piglets (baby boars) (4)
- ☐ Rabbits (4)
- ☐ Woodpecker

Find Out More
on page 28

Fox

A fox will pounce on its prey like a cat.

Badger

This expert digger has powerful claws. It also has webs between its toes. The webs help it tunnel through the soil.

Hedgehog

A hedgehog is covered with pointy spines. When in danger, it curls up into a prickly ball.

Owl

Owls hunt at night for mice and other small animals. Their large eyes help them to see in the dark.

Deer

Deer are fast runners. A baby deer is called a fawn.

Bat

Bats are the only mammals that can fly. They have furry bodies. Their wings are covered with skin, not feathers.

Pheasant

A female pheasant makes her nest on the ground. Her dull color blends in with the leaves on the forest floor. The color of her eggs does, too.

Boar

Wild boars are members of the pig family. The males may have sharp tusks.

Rain Forest

A rain forest is a very noisy place. High in the treetops, monkeys howl and macaws squawk. Almost two-thirds of the earth's plants and animals live here. It is a wet place. Some rain forests get more than 15 feet of rain each year!

Search & Find®

- ☐ Butterflies (4)
- ☐ Hummingbirds (3)
- ☐ Iguana
- ☐ Monkey hanging by tail
- ☐ Monkey with baby
- ☐ Snake
- ☐ Toucan
- ☐ Turtle

Howler monkey
This monkey's howl sounds like a dog's bark. It can be heard up to a mile away.

Scarlet ibis
The scarlet ibis (EYE-bus) uses its long, curved bill to probe water and mud for food.

Tapir
The tapir (TAY-pir) has small eyes, short ears and legs, and a long snout.

Macaw
Macaws are parrots with red, orange, yellow, and blue feathers.

Poison dart frog
This frog's bright colors warn other animals not to eat it. It is very poisonous.

Jaguar
The jaguar is the biggest cat in North and South America.

Find Out More
on page 28

Lily pads
Lily pads are the floating leaves of water lily plants. Some small frogs like to sit on lily pads.

Desert

The desert is a very dry place. Some areas are rocky. Others are covered with sand. Most are very hot. Some creatures live underground to escape the heat. They come out at night, when it is cooler. Insects, mammals, reptiles, birds, spiders, and scorpions all live in the desert.

Search & Find®

- ☐ Birds (5)
- ☐ Butterfly
- ☐ Desert hares (3)
- ☐ Lizards (7)
- ☐ Snakes (2)
- ☐ Tortoise

Bobcat

The bobcat was named for its short, or bobbed, tail. This 20-pound cat has a fierce growl.

Gila monster

The Gila (HEE-la) monster is one of only two lizards that are poisonous.

Sidewinder

It is hard for a snake to grip the sand. This desert rattlesnake moves by making S-shaped curves.

Tarantula

The big, hairy tarantula (tuh-RAN-chuh-lah) does not spin a web. It catches prey by chasing after it.

Desert fox

Foxes hunt at night for small mammals, birds, and reptiles.

Scorpion

Scorpions are related to spiders. Each one has a poisonous stinger on the end of its tail.

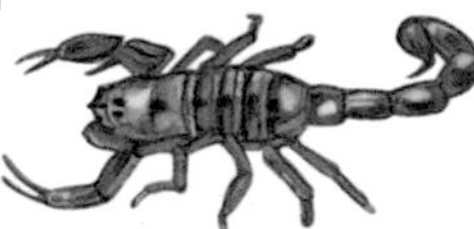

Peccary

The peccary (PEH-kuh-ree) is a relative of the pig and has short tusks that point straight down.

Kangaroo rat

Kangaroo rats have large hind feet. This helps keep the rat from sinking into the sand.

Find Out More
on page 29

Flame angelfish

Flame angelfish can be red or orange. They have blue-purple stripes on their body.

Spotted dolphin

Dolphins are very playful. They love to leap out of the water. Sometimes they will ride the waves made by boats.

Starfish

The starfish, also called a sea star, "sees" with a small eyespot at the tip of each arm.

Ocean Life

Come for a dive in the ocean! Here you'll see creatures in all shapes, sizes, and colors. There are tiny seahorses and giant whales. Many colorful fish live around a coral reef. It's a fun place for scuba divers to explore.

Search & Find®

- ☐ Clown fish (3)
- ☐ Jellyfish
- ☐ Octopuses (2)
- ☐ Pelican
- ☐ Rays (2)
- ☐ Sharks (4)
- ☐ Shipwreck
- ☐ Whale

Seahorse

A female seahorse puts her eggs in the male's belly pouch. He carries the eggs for two to three weeks. Then, as many as 200 babies will swim out of his pouch!

Blue-spotted ray

Rays are related to sharks. They have flat fins that look like wings.

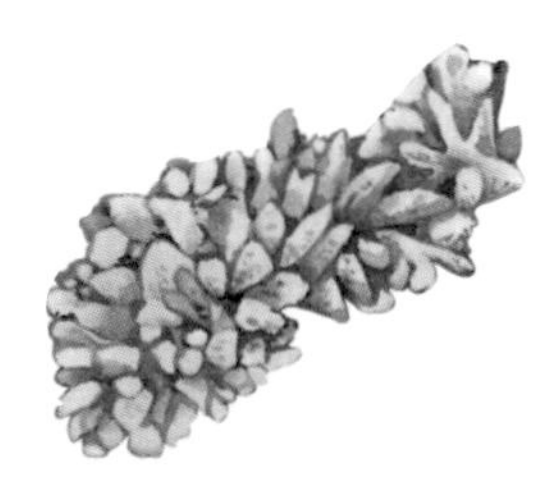

Coral

A coral polyp (PAH-lup) is a tiny ocean animal. It has a skeleton on the outside and a soft body inside. When the body dies, the skeleton remains. Millions and millions of skeletons join to form a reef.

Find Out More
on page 29

Shark

Even before dinosaurs roamed the earth, sharks swam in the sea. Sharks have been around for 400 million years!

Scuba diver

This scuba diver breathes air from a tank on her back. A mask and flippers make it easier to see and move in the water.

African Grassland

The dry grasslands of Africa are called savannas (suh-VAN-uhz). The three largest land animals on Earth live there: the African elephant, the rhinoceros, and the hippopotamus. The savanna is very hot during the day. That's when most of the animals rest.

Search & Fin

- ☐ Baboons (5)
- ☐ Cheetah
- ☐ Giraffes (9)
- ☐ Hippopotamuses (3)
- ☐ Lion cub
- ☐ Stalking lion
- ☐ Warthog

Hyenas

When hyenas (hye-EE-nuz) get excited, they make a high-pitched noise. It sounds like giggling.

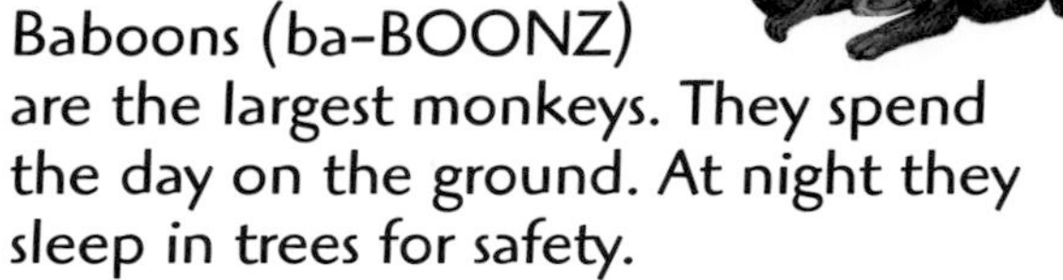

Baboons

Baboons (ba-BOONZ) are the largest monkeys. They spend the day on the ground. At night they sleep in trees for safety.

African elephant

The African elephant is the largest land animal. It is bigger than the Asian elephant.

Lion

A group of lions is called a pride. Only male lions have a mane. Female lions do most of the hunting.

Giraffes

A male giraffe can be 18 feet tall. Giraffes use their long tongues to eat thorny leaves from the tops of trees.

Rhinoceros

A rhinoceros (rye-NAH-suh-rus) has thick skin and short legs. It looks like a tank!

Zebra

Each zebra has its own pattern of stripes. No two zebras are alike.

Hippopotamus

Hippopotamus (hip-oh-PAH-tuh-mus) means "river horse." A hippo spends most of its day in the water. It leaves the water at night to eat grass and plants.

Find Out More
on page 30

Mountains

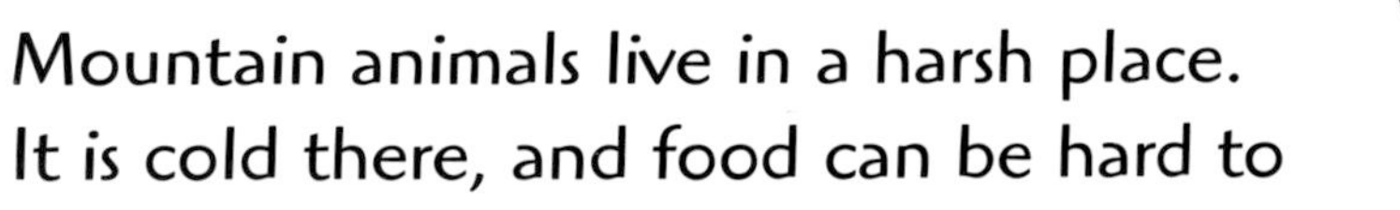

Mountain animals live in a harsh place. It is cold there, and food can be hard to find. The mammals have thick fur to keep them warm. They are very good at climbing the rugged peaks. Fewer plants and animals live on the higher parts of a mountain.

Search & Find®

- ☐ Bird nest
- ☐ Birds in flight (6)
- ☐ Eagle standing on ledge
- ☐ Pika eating a flower
- ☐ Pine trees (2)
- ☐ Pouncing snow leopard
- ☐ White flowers (4)

Find Out More
on page 30

Marmot
A marmot (MAR-mut) has a short, bushy tail and small ears.

Yak
A yak is a type of wild ox. It can live higher up than any other mammal. Yaks are protected from the cold by a thick, furry coat.

Snow leopard
Snow leopards are very rare. They have been hunted for their beautiful fur.

Golden eagle
The golden eagle is a large, powerful bird. It has huge wings that help it fly around the windy mountains.

Ibex
A male ibex is called a ram. It has long, curved horns that can grow up to three feet long!

Alpine flowers
Mountain plants grow in rocky soil and cool temperatures. They need to have strong roots.

Pika
Pikas (PEE-kuhz) have sharp claws that help them climb over rocks.

Under the Ground

Many animals live under the ground. Rabbits and mice dig homes called burrows (BUHR-rohz). They care for their babies there. Some animals sleep in their burrows all winter long. Many spiders, ants, and beetles live underground, too. They provide food for other animals.

Search & Find®

- ☐ Beetles (2)
- ☐ Cricket
- ☐ Dandelion
- ☐ Mice burrows (3)
- ☐ Moles (2)
- ☐ Mushrooms (3)
- ☐ Rabbits (6)

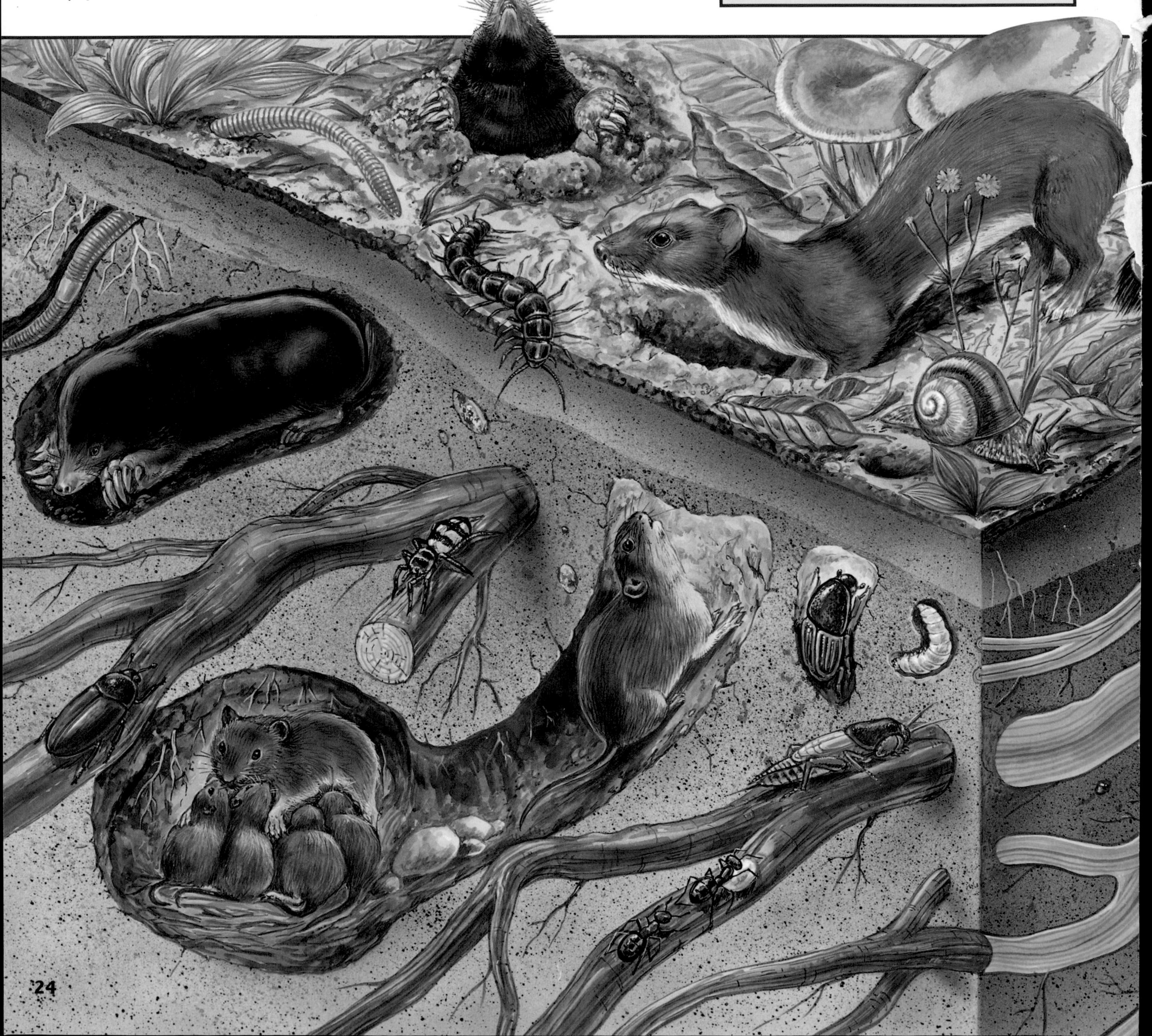

Beetle

There are about 300,000 different kinds of beetles. They make up one-fourth of all the animal life on Earth!

Burrow

A burrow is a hole in the ground made by an animal. Many animals make burrows to live in.

Earthworm

An earthworm's tunnels are good for the earth. The tunnels bring air into the soil.

Spider

Spiders have eight legs. They are related to scorpions and ticks.

Snail

Snails have a soft, slimy body inside their hard shell. They can live in water or on land.

Ant

Ants live in a group called a colony (KAH-luh-nee). There can be millions of ants in one colony.

Centipede

This swift hunter eats insects, worms, and slugs. It may have as many as 175 pairs of legs.

Find Out More
on page 31

Dinosaurs

Apatosaurus ate plants without chewing them. It swallowed stones to help grind up the food in its stomach.

Apatosaurus and *Diplodocus* had huge bodies. They also had small heads, long tails, and pencil-shaped teeth.

The spikes on the end of a *Stegosaurus*'s tail could grow up to four feet long.

***Allosaurus* was a ferocious meat eater.**

Tyrannosaurus rex had teeth that were about one inch wide and 6 inches long.

The word *dinosaur* means "terrible lizard."

Dinosaurs ruled the earth for about 200 million years! Most of them died out about 65 million years ago.

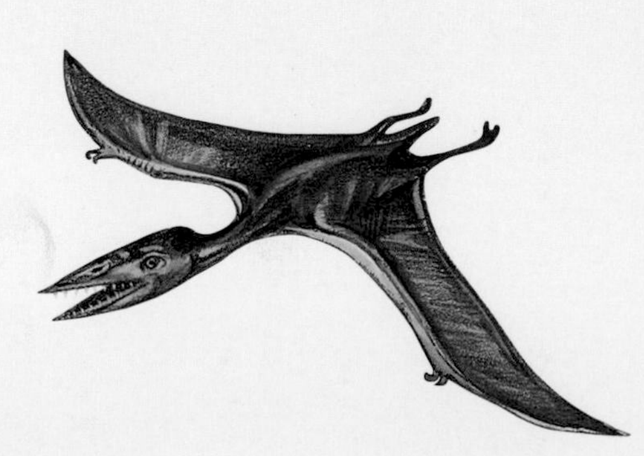

Seasons

All birds start out as eggs.

Squirrels belong to a group of animals called rodents (ROH-dunts). Mice, rats, and beavers are rodents, too.

Baby rabbits are called kittens. A female rabbit usually gives birth to three to six kittens at a time.

Baby birds are most often fed by their parents.

A red fox will eat anything from mice to berries to earthworms. Foxes belong to the same family as dogs.

A baby fox is called a kit or a cub. A female fox is called a vixen.

Polar Regions

Penguins live in a large group called a rookery. One rookery can have thousands of penguins.

Penguins like to have fun! They slide on the snow on their bellies. They like to line up and jump into the water. Then they leap back up and jump again.

Orcas, or killer whales, are found in every ocean in the world.

A walrus uses its tusks to help pull itself out of the water.

A baby walrus is called a calf. A baby seal is called a pup.

Some seals can hold their breath under water for nearly an hour.

A humpback whale can leap clear out of the water. That is called breaching (BREE-ching).

A polar bear has a thick layer of fat under its skin. It also has more fur than any other bear. It even has fur on the soles of its paws!

Forest

A wild boar has an excellent sense of smell. It can sniff out underground foods like roots and bugs. Then it uses its tough snout to dig up food.

Different types of bats eat different things: insects, fruit, fish, or frogs. The vampire bat feeds on the blood of other animals.

Badgers are ferocious fighters. They can even kill and eat poisonous snakes.

An owl cannot move its eyes from side to side. To see things in different directions, it has to turn its head.

Owls have very good hearing.

A group of owls is called a parliament (PAR-luh-mint).

When a baby hedgehog is born, its spines are soft and short. As it grows, the spines get longer and sharper.

Rain Forest

Poison dart frogs are useful to native people. The natives coat their darts with the poison and use them to hunt animals.

A hummingbird can fly backward. It can even hover like a helicopter. No other bird can do that.

Some rain forest spiders are so big they can eat mice and small birds! There are rain forests in Central and South America, Africa, and Southeast Asia.

Macaws often fly in pairs or small groups, called flocks. They warn each other when danger is near.

Jaguars can climb. Sometimes they hunt monkeys in the lower branches of trees.

Desert

A mother scorpion gives birth to as many as thirty-five live babies.

Some scorpions can go a year without eating.

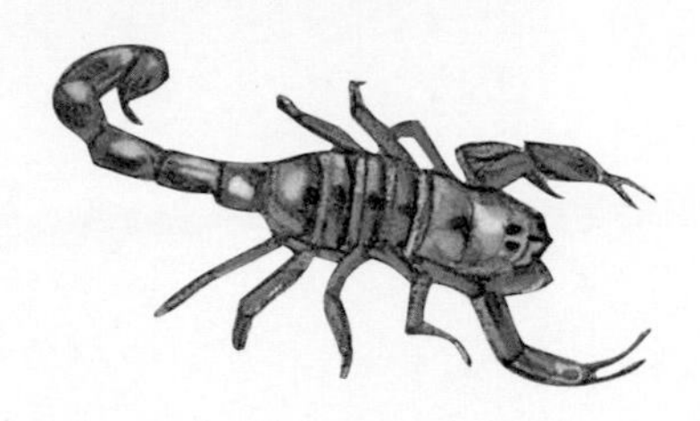

A rattlesnake's rattle can be heard more than 100 feet away.

Coyotes are members of the dog family. When one coyote starts to howl, the others join in.

A coyote can travel 50 miles in a single night!

Desert rats and hares live in burrows in the ground.
A tarantula's powerful jaws can crush a small snake.

Some people keep tarantulas as pets.

Ocean Life

The blue whale is the largest animal to ever live on Earth.

The world's largest coral reef is the Great Barrier Reef in Australia. It can be seen from outer space.

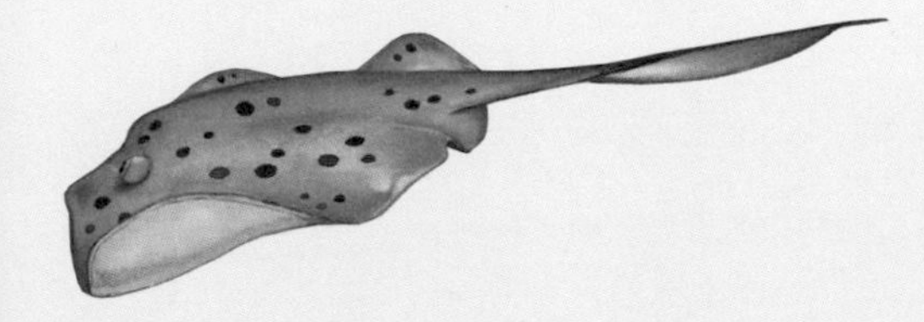

A ray has eyes on top of its head. Its mouth and gills are on the bottom.

There are more than 350 different kinds of sharks. The biggest is the whale shark. It's about 40 feet long. The pygmy shark is only 6 inches long.

A sea turtle cannot pull its head into its shell like a land turtle can.

The snails of the ocean come in many sizes. Some are as small as a grain of sand. Others can be as large as a basketball.

Most starfish have five arms. Some starfish can even grow back an arm that has broken off.

Jellyfish are not actually fish. They have a jelly-like body shaped like an upside-down cup.

African Grassland

Both male and female elephants grow tusks. A tusk can be over 10 feet long!

Hyenas live in packs. A female leads the pack. A hyena's strong jaws can crush bones and horns.

To drink, a giraffe spreads its front legs. It lowers its long neck down to reach the water.

A baby hippo can weigh 100 pounds at birth. An adult can weigh 10,000 pounds.

Antelopes and zebras live in groups called herds. They can run fast. This helps to protect them from lions and other meat eaters.

The word *rhinoceros* means "nose horn." A rhinoceros horn will grow back if it is broken off.

Mountains

Mountain goats have special hooves. This helps them climb and run on the rocks.

Snow leopards are incredible jumpers. They can leap on prey from more than 40 feet away!

Golden eagles learn to fly before they are three months old.

Some bears sleep in a den or cave through the cold winter. They live off their stored body fat.

Marmots live in family groups and "talk" to each other with loud whistles.

Pikas eat grass and small plants. They are related to rabbits.

Under the Ground

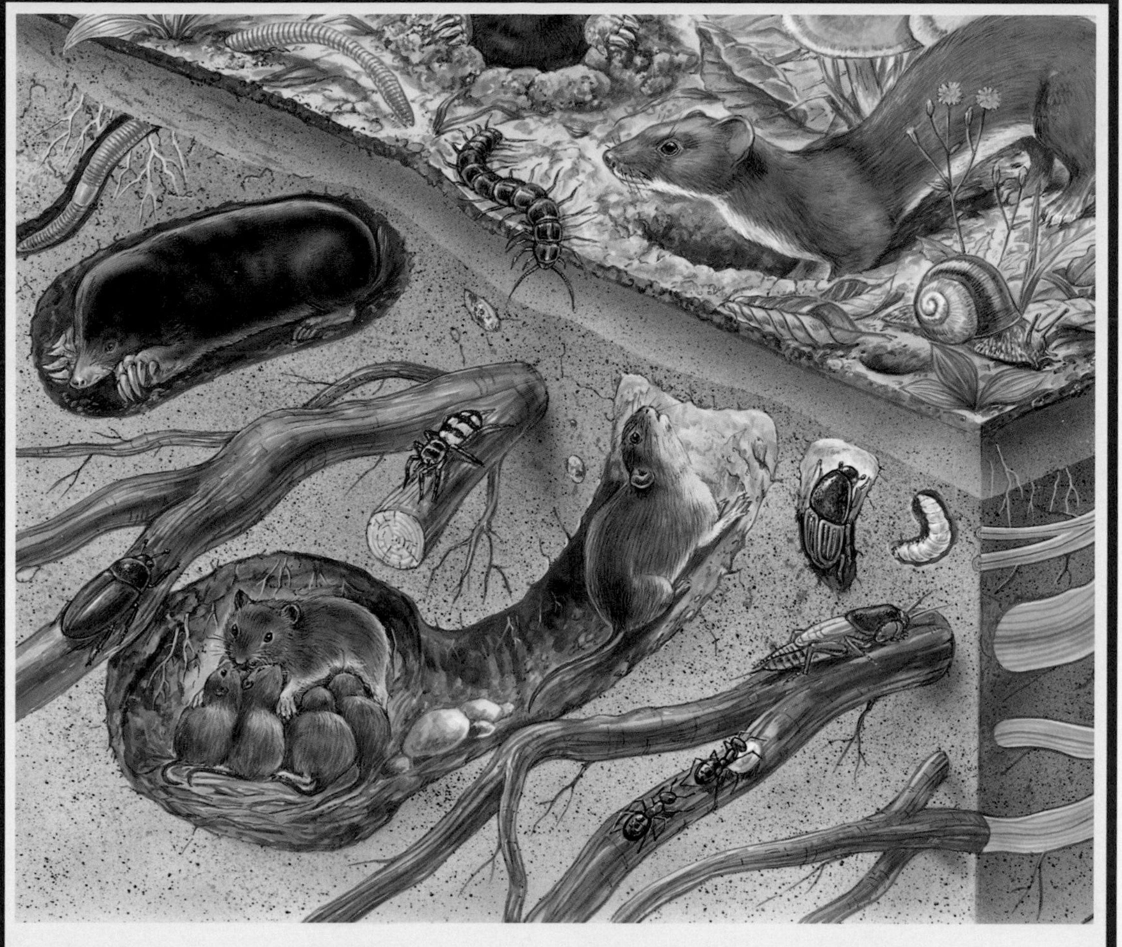

A trapdoor spider lines its burrow with silk. It builds a door on top. When an insect passes, the spider opens the door and attacks.

A giant centipede can be 12 inches long! Its poisonous bite can be dangerous.

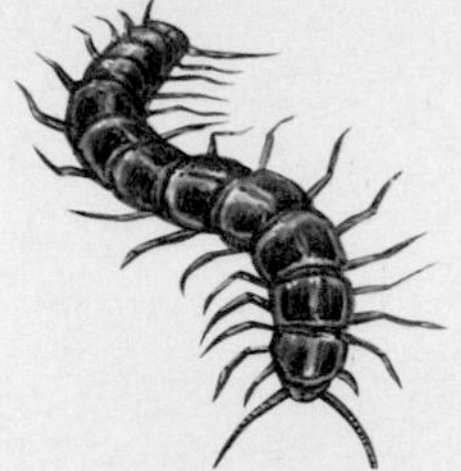

Like all insects, ants have six legs.

The Hercules (HER-kyuh-leez) beetle can be 8 inches long. Some beetles have huge jaws and horns.

Weasels use up a lot of energy. They eat up to half their own body weight each day.

Slugs have slimy bodies like snails. But they don't have the same protective shell.

Moles spend most of the time under the earth. They are nearly blind.

An earthworm has five pairs of hearts.